THE PROMISE OF HIS GLORY